The Little Yellow Boat

Written by Diane Woodrow
Illustrations by Danielle Chapman-Skaines

Bumblebee Books
London

A CIP catalogue record for this title is
available from the British Library.

ISBN: 978-1-83934-204-2

Bumblebee Books is an imprint of
Olympia Publishers.

First Published in 2021

Bumblebee Books
Tallis House
2 Tallis Street
London
EC4Y 0AB

Printed in Great Britain

www.olympiapublishers.com

Dedication

To Ben and Tabitha

The Little Yellow Boat loved to go on adventures on her own. But each time she went away, some disaster would happen. She would return knowing she had failed again.

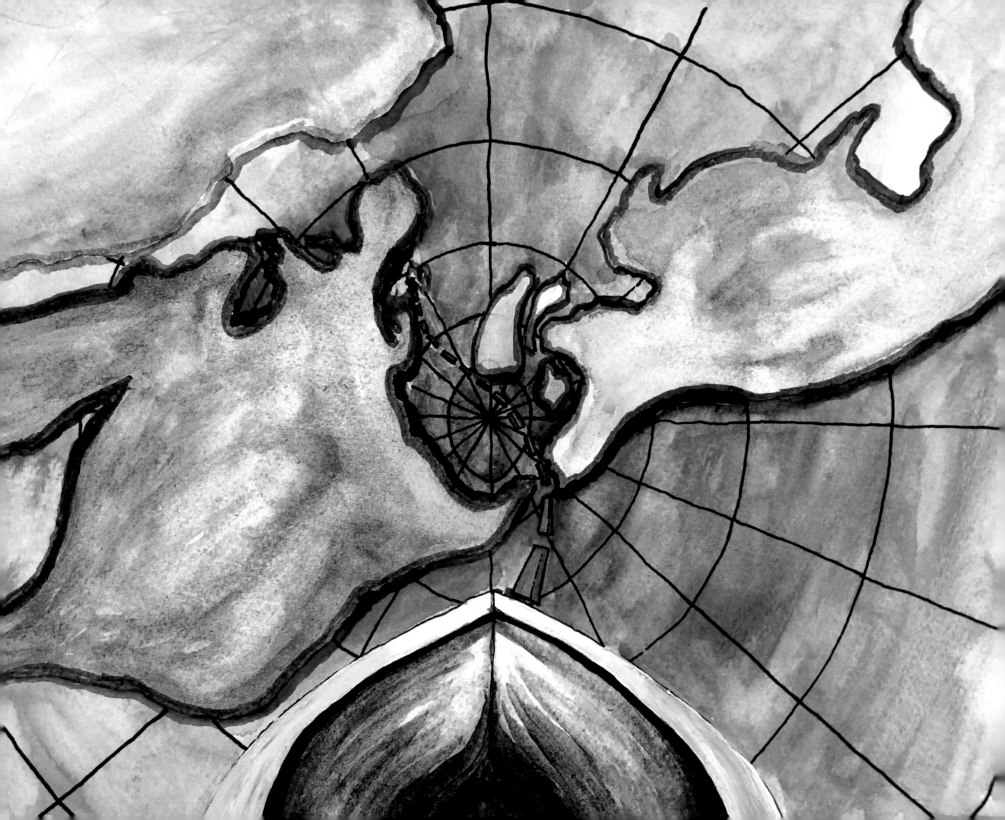

This time she mapped out a clear course.
She made a clear plan.

She held her bows high as she left the harbour. All the other boats watched her. This time she would show them what she was really made of.

She was not far from home when the sky started to darken, and the waves began to swell. Her confidence was ebbing, but she knew she must carry on.

The rain lashed and lashed. She could imagine the whisperings of the other boats she had left behind. She kept repeating, "I can do this alone," to give herself some courage.

The waves were growing higher and stronger.
She rolled and tumbled in the stormy sea.

The darkness grew heavier. The waves grew higher. There was nothing she could get her bearings from.

She closed her eyes. Her salt tears mingled with the ocean. The Little Yellow Boat did not have the strength to carry on. She would have to turn back knowing she had failed again.

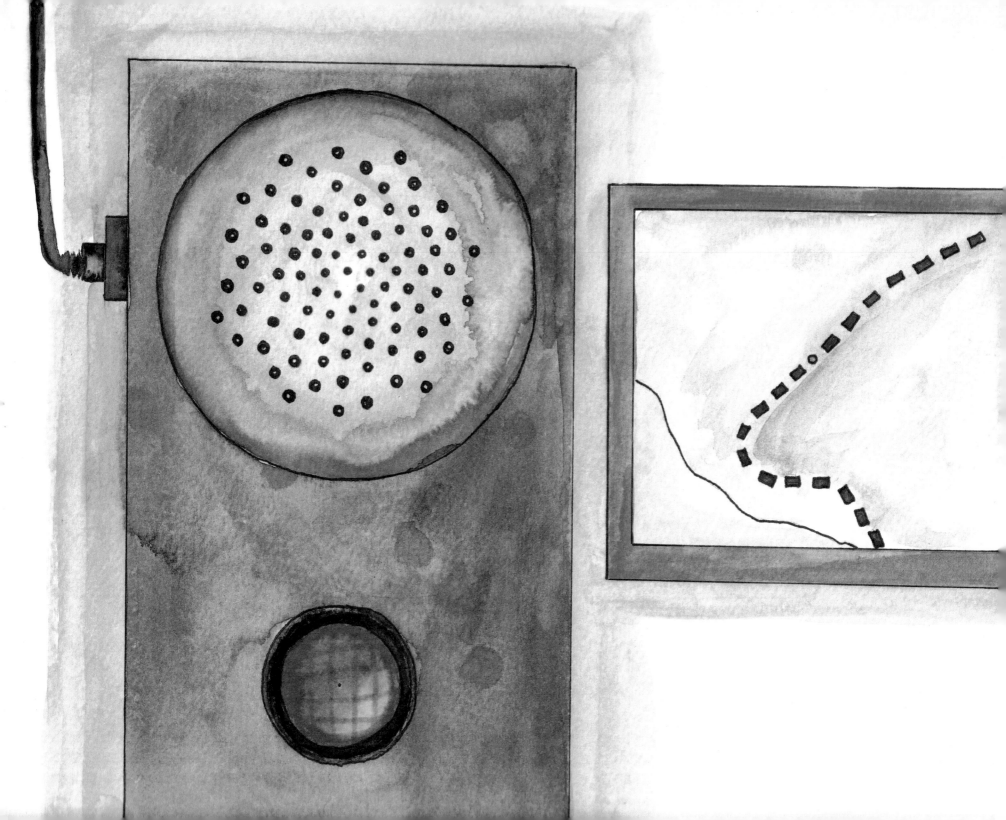

As she rolled in the dark, rough sea a thought came to her. "It's time to ask for help, Little Yellow Boat," she said aloud.

She looked at the radio.

She realised she did not want to be rescued and taken home.

She wanted help to continue with her quest.

She remembered every boat she had ever met.
She thought of how each one had different strengths which could help her carry on.

One by one she got in touch with
the other boats and calmly said what she wanted.
It took much more time than a yell for help.

Each boat offered different pieces of advice; some practical, some directional, some just words of encouragement.

The waves still roared and tossed and rolled but the Little Yellow Boat moved onwards with her journey because she knew she was not travelling alone.

When she eventually returned home, she was wiser and stronger. Now she was part of a community of boats she could help as much as they could help her.

About the Author

As she is walking her dog on the beach near her home in North Wales, Diane Woodrow thinks up stories about the sea, local history and her faith, some of which she blogs about on www.aspirationaladventures.wordpress.com

About the Illustrator

Danielle Chapman-Skaines, otherwise known as Didi, has been producing artwork as a business from a young age. Her travels and training in counselling have enriched and influenced a deep fondness for revealing the inner-heart through watercolour landscapes.

Lightning Source UK Ltd.
Milton Keynes UK
UKRC031003120522
402885UK00001B/1

9 781839 342042